GLISTER

THE

HOUSE HUNT

WALKER BOOKS

DEDICATED TO GREAT AUNTY DOT.
Last of the Butterworths

First published 2009 by Walker Books Ltd
87 Vauxhall Walk, London SE11 5HJ

2 4 6 8 10 9 7 5 3 1

Printed and bound in Italy by  Grafica Veneta S.p.A.

British Library Cataloguing in Publication Data:
a catalogue record for this book is available from the British Library

ISBN 978-1-4063-2049-7

www.walker.co.uk

www.andiwatson.biz

for Clara

Chilblain is no ordinary home. It has a magical sparkle which is missing from a typical two-bedroom semi-detached with off-road parking and en suite bathroom.

No, Chilblain has never been comfortable in its own skin, like a chameleon spinning through the colour wheel or a peacock rearranging its feathers.

New wings appear overnight, stay for a week, then disappear again. Ballrooms come and go. The Egypt Room appeared after tea in 1805 and found it so to its liking that it has stayed ever since.

Grottos hide behind pantry doors; coral and flint in place of tins of baked beans.

Art Nouveau beauties alight on the walls, crowding around the caryatids by the fireplace before continuing their mysterious flight to other lands.

LET THERE BE LIGHT

A Masonic Temple took up residence in the wine cellar and a gaggle of Judges and Chiefs of Police drank themselves to the floor.

And so it was one day that Glister's village, Gravehunger Moss, was entered in the Bonny Village (TM) competition. The winner of the grand prize would be officially twinned with Versailles, France.

GREY GABLES

Glister happened to know Gravehunger Moss was already twinned with villages in Lilliput, Cimmeria, Cockaigne, Shangri-La, Lyonesse, Skull Island and Borsetshire, but not being able to fit them on the village sign and not wishing to be too show-offy, it remained uncelebrated.

Dad apologized for losing his temper, but the fact was neither of them were used to being cooped up together quite so much.

The walls pressed in and the hours stretched out in front of her like stale chewing gum.

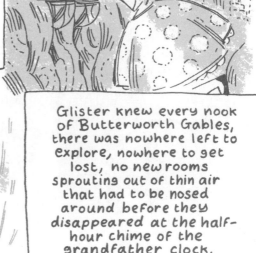

Glister knew every nook of Butterworth Gables, there was nowhere left to explore, nowhere to get lost, no new rooms sprouting out of thin air that had to be nosed around before they disappeared at the half-hour chime of the grandfather clock.

She felt like her best friend had moved to a new school.

She was lonely.

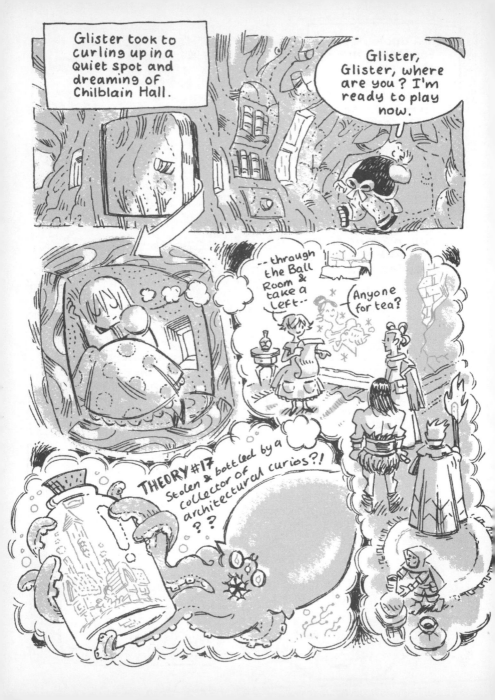

A good dream did visit her that night.

Philippa Veil, ghostly author, had written her a letter.

My dear friend,
    I feel I must write to tell you, for how else shall you know, that our home, Chilblain Hall, has lately taken to wandering. In no small part, I think, due to its low spirits.

    You must feel its absence most keenly and I make mention of you very often. As for myself, I must own, I am greatly enjoying my travels, having never had the opportunity in my first life.

    But I am running on so and must tell you all that has passed since we were parted. Oh, where to begin?

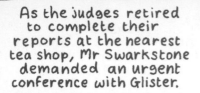

As the judges retired to complete their reports at the nearest tea shop, Mr Swarkstone demanded an urgent conference with Glister.

I have it on good authority, from an inside source, that it's neck and neck between Gravehunger and Widowfield for the Bonny Village crown. This could decide it. Can't you get Chilblain back here, for the good of the village?

Its pride's been wounded and only an apology will settle it.

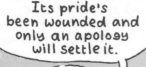

An apology to...to a... MANGY...

...to a unique historic house?

We have notepaper inside.

With the Bonny Village trophy within his grasp, Mr Swarkstone swallowed his pride. Glister entrusted the letter to one of Long Meg's sisters who promised to deliver it in person.

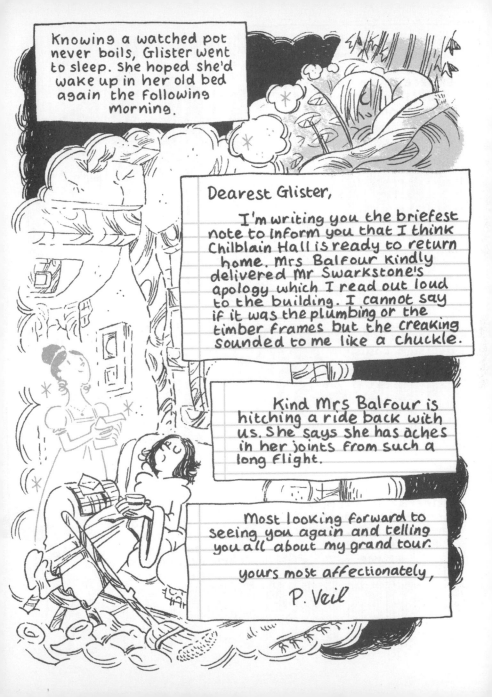

Glister's dad was unsure of how to feel about Chilblain's return at first, but soon warmed again to his old home.

It's grand to have you back where you belong. Now, no more of this gallivanting off around the planet, do you hear?

Your duty is to Gravehunger and the Butterworths, and let it be said, I find your siding with Widowfield and Clatteringshire to be grossly disloyal.

County and village must count for something.

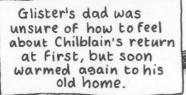

The venerable building shivered indignantly. It had the look of a displeased swan about to take flight.

Dad, um, I promised the hall that it could take a holiday every year.

It's the people who are supposed to take holidays, not the wretched house they live in.

You did what?

It was going to stay in Widowfield unless I promised.

It's only for a week, and it has to book in advance with us first.

The Toll Troll cursed his foul luck and bedded down in the Hen House.

SHOO!

BWAK BWAK BWAK

By which time Glister had recovered her lustre.

The End

Chilblain Hall and the Sunday Painters

One day, not so long ago, there was much excitement at Chilblain Hall. Laurence Sunday had chosen the ancient pile to be the subject of a painting masterclass. Laurence was a very popular watercolourist, a favourite with ladies of a certain age who were known as his Sunday Painters.

On a perfect day for painting, blue skies above with only a smattering of fluffy white cloud, Laurence Sunday made his grand entrance – to the delight of his cooing and adoring fans.

The charming and unflappable painter had the crowd's full attention as he expertly sketched Chilblain Hall. He briefly turned his back on Chilblain to address the ladies.

"One must delight in the details – take the crooked tower, for instance," Laurence suggested.

Chilblain instantly became self-conscious about its crooked tower and when Laurence turned back he was shocked to see the tower was now straight. Confused but determined, he began applying his first washes of colour.

"Pay particular attention to the composition," Laurence instructed.

The sun dipped behind a small cloud, leaving Chilblain in the shade. The Hall shuffled itself over to be back in the light. When Laurence glanced up from his work Chilblain was partly obscured from his view by a tree. The painter's eyes grew wide in surprise. He sipped from his painting water by mistake, mopped his brow and hurriedly explained how darker colours could be used to cover mistakes. He quickly daubed a tree into the foreground of his painting.

By now the cloud that had obscured Chilblain had passed over but another one was threatening to come between the hall and the sun. Chilblain scooted back to its original position. When Laurence looked up again there was no longer a tree between him and the old building. He began to lose his cool, standing up and angrily addressing the crowd.

"Is this some form of juvenile prank?" he demanded, reddening in the face.

Recovering himself, Laurence sat back at his easel intending to quickly finish the picture and enjoy a long lie down. Chilblain could stand it no longer, itching with curiosity, it hopped forward to get a look at the painting. Laurence frowned at the long shadow that was suddenly cast over his work. He looked up slowly and saw the tower of Chilblain Hall leaning at a dangerous angle, almost on top of him. Laurence jumped out of his seat in shock, knocking his water, pigments and brushes all over himself and his painting. The painter and his followers scrambled away in panic, leaving the remains of the painting behind for Chilblain Hall to admire.

A little extra GLISTER...

Philippa Veil's

BRUSSELS

POSTCARD

Although the Cathedral is delightful, the city holds itself in high regard. Too much like Bath for my liking.

Yours affectionately,

P. Veil

Post Card

Entranced by the architecture, bemused by the art.

Your friend,

P. Veil

Glister
Butterworth

Gravehunger
Moss

WORCESTER

Am much enamoured with the exceptional pastries. Wrote five hundred words from the bell tower of Notre Dame. Trés belle!

Best wishes,

P. Veil

Bilbao

112266

Postcards

Chilblain wilting in heat. In Moscow by time finished writing this.

Yours with best wishes,

P. Veil

Not a nook or cranny for Chilblain to squeeze into. Settled below ground. Very cramped.

Yours affectionately,

P. Veil

Glister Butterworth
Gravehunger
Moss

Down to last tea bag. Hoping to turn Chilblain's thoughts to home.

Yours fearfully,

P. Veil

Glister the Faerie Host

When boundary changes mean Faerieland moves next door to Chilblain Hall, Glister's father wants her to be extra careful.

DO NOT CROSS

They can be good neighbours and they can be bad neighbours, but they're the best neighbours when they're left alone.

Life becomes stranger still when Glister's long lost mum appears in her mirror.

Glister is delighted.

We should have a party.

Andi Watson grew up in a small town in West Yorkshire. It's a nice place but a bit dull so he watched too much telly, read a lot and enjoyed filling blank sheets of paper with drawings of space battles. He's always loved stories, drawing and books so when he re-discovered comics while at art school he found he'd stumbled on the perfect way to combine all the things he likes to do. What he enjoys most about *Glister* is the freedom to create any kind of story and follow funny ideas wherever they lead.

Some of his favourite things are: Hayao Miyazaki films, cake, cups of tea, second-hand book shops, depressing music, brussels sprouts, chocolate, long-tailed tits and fairy tales.

Andi has been nominated for the prestigious Eisner Award and Harvey Award which both recognize outstanding works in comics and sequential art.

He's worked in a variety of genres, from sci-fi and fantasy to contemporary drama, romantic comedy and now stories for children.

He lives in Worcester with his wife and daughter. *Glister* is his first series for Walker Books.

www.andiwatson.biz